BOOK OF MORMON
Songs for CHILDREN

Music by **LYNN S. LUND**

Lyrics by **MABEL JONES GABBOTT**
GERALD N. LUND • **SHAWN M. STRINGHAM**

Stories by **GERALD N. LUND**
Illustrated by **LESTER LEE**

BOOKCRAFT
Salt Lake City, Utah

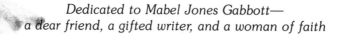

Dedicated to Mabel Jones Gabbott—
a dear friend, a gifted writer, and a woman of faith

ISBN 1-57008-272-3

First Printing, 1996

Printed in the United States of America

CONTENTS

THE BOOK OF MORMON IS A WITNESS

For many, many years after Jesus died and was resurrected, his church was not upon the earth. People forgot about God. Many, many people did not have a chance to have the gospel in their lives. Heavenly Father had a plan to bring the gospel back to the earth and to have the Church of Jesus Christ here once again. This is called the Restoration because he restored, or brought back, what had been lost.

One of the most important parts of the Restoration was the coming forth of the Book of Mormon. Joseph Smith got the gold plates that contained the Book of Mormon record even before the priesthood was restored. The Book of Mormon was translated and published before the Church was organized. We had the Book of Mormon before we had temples, or the Word of Wisdom, or twelve Apostles. The Book of Mormon was a very important part of God's plan of restoration.

One of the reasons the Book of Mormon is so important is that it is a new witness for Jesus Christ. We have the Bible which teaches us about Jesus, and it is important to us. But we have another book that also teaches us about the Savior. It teaches us about his mission. It teaches us his gospel. It testifies to his resurrection and that he still lives today. Without the Book of Mormon, there is much about Jesus that we would not know.

We should thank our Heavenly Father for giving us the Book of Mormon, because it is a witness of his Son, Jesus Christ. (See Title Page, Book of Mormon.)

THE BOOK OF MORMON IS A WITNESS

GERALD N. LUND

LYNN S. LUND

tells me he's the Son of God, who died to save all men. It
tells great things the Lord has done and what his proph-ets heard. I

tells me of the i-ron rod_____ And how to live with
can draw clos-er to God's Son_____ By feast-ing on its

him. The words._____

THE BOOK OF MORMON IS RESTORED

One night in September 1823, a seventeen-year-old boy knelt in prayer in his bedroom. Joseph Smith had been visited by Heavenly Father and Jesus three years earlier. Now he wanted to know if Heavenly Father was still pleased with him. As he prayed, suddenly a light began to fill his room. At first Joseph was afraid, for all at once there was a person in his room, standing in the air above the floor. But soon the fear left Joseph, for he knew this was an angel of God. His face and clothes were white and so bright they looked like the lightning that fills the sky on a stormy night.

The angel called Joseph by name and told him that he had come from the presence of God to give Joseph a message. He said that his name was Moroni. The message had to do with a set of gold plates that was buried in a hill nearby. Three more times that night and the next morning Moroni came to Joseph. Finally, Joseph went to the hill where Moroni had showed him to go. There he found the gold plates. Though he was not allowed to take them out for four more years, finally Joseph got the plates from Moroni and translated them. This became the Book of Mormon.

Since 1830, when it was first published, millions of copies of the Book of Mormon have been printed and sent throughout the world. Thousands of people have come to know that Jesus is the Christ by reading the Book of Mormon. The Book of Mormon was one of the most important things to happen in the Restoration. (See Joseph Smith—History 1:27–54.)

THE BOOK OF MORMON IS RESTORED

MABEL JONES GABBOTT

LYNN S. LUND

The rec-ords wait-ed in the hill   Un-til the time they should come forth.

These scrip-tures tes-ti-fy of Christ.   The Book of Mor-mon is re-

rit.

1.
stored.

2.
stored.

LEHI AND HIS FAMILY

Six hundred years before Jesus was born, a prophet named Lehi lived in Jerusalem with his wife, Sariah. He had four sons—Laman, Lemuel, Nephi, and Sam. He also had daughters. The Lord warned Lehi in a dream that Jerusalem was going to be destroyed and told him to take his family and flee into the wilderness. Laman and Lemuel were angry, but Nephi prayed to God and learned for himself that this is what the Lord wanted.

After they fled into the wilderness, the Lord told Lehi to send his sons back to get the brass plates. These were like our Bible and were important to Lehi's family. The Lord also told Lehi to have his sons go and get Ishmael and his family to come with them, which they did.

Lehi's group went into the desert where there were no roads and no people. It would have been easy for them to get lost and to die. But God prepared a wonderful compass for Lehi and his family. It was outside Lehi's tent one morning when he woke up. It had arrows on it and pointed the direction they should go in the wilderness. It was called the Liahona. It only worked when they were righteous. Because of God's love, Lehi and his family finally came to the promised land.

Just as God gave Lehi a compass to guide him, we are given the Holy Ghost to guide us in life and show us what to do. We too have to be righteous to have the Holy Ghost in our lives. (See 1 Nephi 1–17.)

LEHI AND HIS FAMILY

GERALD N. LUND

LYNN S. LUND

Le - hi and his fam - 'ly trust - ed in the Lord. He told them they must go in - to the
God gave them a com - pass that would show the way. It worked by faith and guid - ed them both

wil - der - ness. Leav - ing all be - hind them, show - ing God their faith, They
day and night. Like the Li - a - ho - na, we too have a guide. The

knew that they must fol - low him in righ - teous - ness. Then God said:
Ho - ly Spir - it al - ways helps us choose the right. Then God says:

"I will be your light, And I'll pre - pare the way. And I will lead you safe - ly to the

prom - ised land." And if we choose the right in all we do and say, Then

God will guide us safe - ly home. home.

THANK YOU, NEPHI

When Lehi told his family they were going to leave their beautiful home and go into the wilderness, Laman and Lemuel were angry. They did not believe the Lord had told their father to leave. But Nephi, who was the youngest brother, prayed to the Lord and found out that what his father said was true.

Though sometimes it was very hard, Nephi decided he would always do what the Lord asked. He once said: "I will go and do the things which the Lord hath commanded, for I know that the Lord giveth no commandments unto the children of men, save he shall prepare a way for them that they may accomplish the thing which he commandeth them."

Nephi went back to Jerusalem and got the plates of brass. He built a ship that took his family to the promised land. He became the leader of his people, who were called the Nephites. He wrote the story of his family and of how the Lord had blessed them. He was faithful and true to God his whole life.

When we study the life of Nephi we learn that the Lord greatly blesses those who are obedient to Him. Because of this important lesson, today we can say, "Thank you, Nephi." (See 1 Nephi 1–4, 17.)

THANK YOU, NEPHI

MABEL JONES GABBOTT

LYNN S. LUND

Thank you, Ne - phi, for your words that tell the
Thank you, Ne - phi. Long a - go you stopped be -

plain.   And   when   you   had   a   task   to
word. _____ Thank you, Ne - phi. All your

do,   you   lis - tened   to   the   Lord's   com -
days   you   walked   in   truth;   you   loved   the

1.

mand.

2.

Lord. _____

-13-

ENOS KNELT TO PRAY

After coming to the promised land, Lehi's family continued to grow. One of Lehi's grandsons was named Enos. Enos was born in the land of America. There weren't many people in the promised land yet. There were no large cities. And many of the people got food by hunting in the forests and jungles. One day while Enos was out all alone hunting, he began to think about the things his father had taught him about Heavenly Father and Jesus.

Suddenly, Enos wanted more than anything else to know if these things were true. He decided to pray about them. But Enos didn't just kneel down and pray for a few minutes. He prayed all day long. Even after it got dark, he kept on praying to his Heavenly Father. Finally, after many hours, the Lord spoke to Enos and told him his sins were forgiven. From Enos, the son of Jacob, we learn that the Lord hears and answers our prayers when we have faith in him and pray with all our hearts for the good things we need. (See Enos 1.)

ENOS KNELT TO PRAY

SHAWN M. STRINGHAM

LYNN S. LUND

E - nos, son of Ja - cob, prayed when he hunt-ed in the woods. He asked
heard God say to him, "You're for - giv - en of your sins, For your

God to grant him faith And to teach him to be good.
faith has made you whole." Then he felt God's love with - in.

E - nos knelt to pray when the sun was high,

And kept pray-ing through the night. Soon he came to

feel the Sav - ior by his side. Then he knew his heart was

1.
right.

2.
E - nos right.

KING BENJAMIN

About a hundred years before Jesus was born, there lived a righteous king whose name was King Benjamin. One day, King Benjamin told his son Mosiah that he was getting old and wanted to speak to his people once more before he died. He told his son that he had a special name he wanted to give the people. His son sent word and told all the people to come to the temple in the city of Zarahemla to hear King Benjamin. There were so many people that King Benjamin had a large tower built so more could see and hear him.

King Benjamin told his people many things. He told them that when they served others, they were also serving God. He told them to remember all the blessings they had received from their Heavenly Father. Most important, King Benjamin taught his people about Jesus Christ, how he would die to take away their sins, and how they could be more like Jesus in the way they lived.

The people were so touched by the words of King Benjamin that their hearts were changed and they didn't want to do anything bad ever again. King Benjamin said that because their hearts were changed, it was like they had become the sons and daughters of Christ. This was the new name he gave to his people. He called them the children of Christ. When we have our hearts changed so we love Heavenly Father and always try to choose the right, we are the children of Christ too. (See Mosiah 2–5.)

KING BENJAMIN

MABEL JONES GABBOTT

LYNN S. LUND

king, be - lov - ed Ben - ja - min, would speak to them and they would hear.
help each oth - er to be kind and walk in good - ness day by day.

mf

"Be - lieve in God," he said to them. "Be - lieve that he will send his Son, To

heal the blind and com - fort the sick, And give his life for ev - 'ry - one."

We be - lieve, oh, we be - lieve In Je - sus Christ, the Son of

God.　　And we'll be called the chil-dren of Christ,　The sons and daugh-ters

of＿＿＿ the Lord.

The peo-ple

ABINADI AND KING NOAH

About the same time that King Benjamin lived, a group of Nephites went to live in the same country as the Lamanites. They were led by a man named Zeniff. He was a good man and loved God. But when he died, his son became king. His name was Noah, and he was very wicked. He made the people work to support him. He drank lots of wine and did other evil things.

One day the Lord sent a prophet to the people of King Noah. This prophet's name was Abinadi. He was not afraid to tell the people how bad they were. He even told them how wicked their king was and that if he didn't repent, his life would be taken. This made the people of Noah very angry. They took ropes and tied up Abinadi and brought him to King Noah. Noah said Abinadi had to take back what he had said or he would be killed. Abinadi told King Noah that he had said only those things which the Lord had told him to say and that he would not take back any of it. Abinadi was filled with great power, and no one dared touch him until he was through speaking.

Then they took Abinadi and burned him to death because he would not take back his words. Abinadi died because he did what the Lord asked him to do rather than what men asked him to do. Abinadi is a great example of faith and courage for us to follow. (See Mosiah 11–17.)

ABINADI AND KING NOAH

MABEL JONES GABBOTT

LYNN S. LUND

bin - a - di went to the court to tell King No - ah to re - pent. He
No - ah had his wick - ed priests take ropes and tie A - bin - a - di. This

was a proph-et wise and true. By heav-en's or-ders he was sent. King
proph-et stood with cour-age brave. They lit the fire and watched him die. King

No-ah told his wick-ed priests: "Tie up this man who talks this way." They
No-ah nev-er did re-pent. One day he died by fire,___ too. A-

could not touch A - bin-a-di, Un-til he said what he did
bin-a-di spoke for the Lord. And all the proph-et said came

1.
say.

2.
King true.___

ALMA AND AMULEK

Alma the Younger was named after his father, Alma, who was the head of the Church. At first, Alma the Younger did not do as his father wished. In fact, Alma the Younger was so bad that he was not allowed to be a member of the Church anymore. Finally an angel came to him and told him that if he continued to be bad, he would be destroyed. Alma the Younger was converted to the Lord after that experience, and for the rest of his life he served God. He even became the prophet and head of the Church.

One day, Alma was doing missionary work among the Nephites. He had a companion named Amulek. They were in a city that was filled with wicked men and women. They arrested Alma and Amulek and threw them into prison. These wicked men also killed the women and children who believed Alma and Amulek's message, and they made Alma and Amulek watch.

Then one day, while the wicked men were in the prison shouting and yelling at Alma and Amulek, the Lord gave the two missionaries great power. Alma and Amulek broke off the ropes that bound them. A great earthquake shook the building. The walls came crashing down and killed the wicked men, but Alma and Amulek were not hurt. When we read about Alma and Amulek we see that even though sometimes we are tested, if we are obedient the Lord will still watch over us. (See Alma 8, 14.)

ALMA AND AMULEK

MABEL JONES GABBOTT

LYNN S. LUND

Al - ma and Am - u - lek were mis - sion - ar - ies. Al - ma and Am - u - lek
Al - ma and Am - u - lek were cast in pris - on. Al - ma and Am - u - lek

preached God's word. They fol - lowed God's com - mands in teach - ing the gos - pel plan.
knelt and prayed. God heard their fer - vent calls, and down fell the pris - on walls.

No one be-lieved in the words they heard.
Al - ma and Am - u - lek both they were saved.

When I am called to be a mis-sion-ar-y,

I'll preach the gos-pel and serve the Lord. Wheth - er I'm sent next door, or

called to some dis - tant shore, I'll read the scrip - tures and teach God's word.

AMMON AND KING LAMONI

Mosiah became the king over the Nephites after the death of his father, King Benjamin. King Mosiah had four sons who were very wicked. They were with Alma the Younger when the angel appeared to him. Like Alma, they were converted to the Lord after that. They decided they wanted to be missionaries to the Lamanites, even though this was very dangerous. They wanted to make up for the bad things they had done.

The leader of the four sons of Mosiah was named Ammon. Ammon and his brothers went to the land of the Lamanites and then split up to go to different places. As soon as the Lamanites saw Ammon, they tied him up and took him to their king. The king, whose name was Lamoni, was a wicked man, and sometimes would kill Nephites who were brought to him. But Ammon was not afraid. When the king asked him what he was doing there, Ammon said he wanted to live among the Lamanites and be part of them. This pleased the king very much, and he made Ammon one of his servants. Ammon didn't say anything yet about being a missionary.

Three days later, Ammon proved he was a friend of the king when he saved the king's flocks from some robbers. King Lamoni was so touched that he let Ammon preach the gospel to him. When King Lamoni learned about Jesus and how He died for his sins, he and all of his household were converted. The sons of Mosiah preached to the Lamanites for fourteen years and converted many thousands to the Church. We can learn an important lesson from Ammon. Ammon showed us that if we are a good example to others, they may want to live more like Jesus. (See Mosiah 27–28, Alma 17–26.)

AMMON AND KING LAMONI

MABEL JONES GABBOTT

LYNN S. LUND

This is a song a-bout Am-mon, Who tend-ed the flocks of the
This is a song a-bout Am-mon, Who stood in the court of the
This is a song a-bout Am-mon, A ser-vant of Je-sus, the

king, Who fright-ened the bad men with his cour-age And a
king. He said, "Do you know a-bout the Sav-ior? I can
Lord, A proph-et with pow-er and with wis-dom Who could

small stone that fit in a sling. The ser-vants ran off to the
tell you of mar-vel-ous things." He told them that Je-sus, a
teach men the Lord's ho-ly word. — This is a song a-bout

court-yard, To tell King La-mo-ni the truth. How___
ba-by, Would be born in far Beth-le-hem. Christ would
Am-mon, Who loved and be-lieved in the Lord. King La-

Am-mon had saved the king's for-tune, Be-
teach us to love one an-oth-er, And
mo-ni and all of his peo-ple Be-

cause of his faith and his youth.
one day would die for all men.
lieved and ac-cept-ed God's word.

MORONI TORE HIS COAT

Not many years before the birth of Christ, things in the Nephite nation began to be very bad. The Nephites were at constant war with the Lamanites. Many of the Nephites had forgotten the promises they had made with the Lord. At this time, the Nephites had a great leader named Moroni. Moroni was not only a brave man and a good soldier but also a man of great faith in the Lord. Because of his success in helping the Nephites in battle, they made him the chief captain over all their armies.

When a very wicked man tried to become king of the Nephites and take away the freedom of the people, Moroni was very angry. Many Nephites had given their lives in the war to protect their liberty. Moroni had an idea. He took one of his coats and tore a piece of cloth from it. Then he wrote on it in big letters: "In memory of our God, our religion, and freedom, and our peace, our wives, and our children." These were the things that were most important to him and to the Nephites. He tied the cloth to a pole and called it the "title of liberty" because it reminded the people of the liberties and freedoms that were so important to them.

When the people saw Moroni's title of liberty, thousands of them came to help fight for their freedom. Had it not been for Moroni and the title of liberty, the Nephites would have lost everything that was most important to them. Sometimes we have to have the courage to fight for the things which matter most to us. (See Alma 46–47.)

MORONI TORE HIS COAT

MABEL JONES GABBOTT

LYNN S. LUND

all the peo - ple called: "Ti - tle of Lib - er- ty." Stand up for lib - er- ty.
we can wave our own "Ti - tle of Lib - er - ty."

Stand up for truth. We stand for free - dom, for we are God's youth.

We'll wave our ban - ners high. We'll join Mo - ro - ni's cry. Stand up for lib - er- ty, For we are God's

youth.   Mo -   youth.

TWO THOUSAND SONS OF HELAMAN

When Ammon and his companions converted thousands of the Lamanites, these converts decided to make a special promise to the Lord. They took their swords and spears and their bows and arrows and buried them deep in the earth. "Never again will we go to war," they said. "This is our solemn promise."

A few years later, there were great wars between the Lamanites and the Nephites. It looked like the Lamanites were going to win. The Lamanites who had been converted earlier, now called the people of Ammon, felt very sad. The Nephites needed help, but they couldn't help them because of their promise. But then they had an idea. The people of Ammon had many young sons who had not made the same promise as their parents. Two thousand of these young men came to Helaman and told him they wanted to help the Nephites.

Helaman was amazed and yet very pleased. Not only were these young men brave and strong, but their mothers had taught them to have great faith in God. Helaman took his youthful army out to see if they could help the Nephites. Helaman so loved these young men that he called them his sons.

Soon the young men were caught in the middle of a great battle. The sons of Helaman fought with such great courage that the Nephites won that day. To everyone's surprise, Helaman found that not one of his two thousand sons had been killed. Because of their great faith, they had been protected by Heavenly Father. The two thousand sons of Helaman helped the Nephites save their freedom and their liberty. (See Alma 53, 56–58.)

TWO THOUSAND SONS OF HELAMAN

GERALD N. LUND

LYNN S. LUND

cher - ished free - dom more than life. They served with loy - al - ty. They
fought the foe with strength from God. They served him val - iant - ly. And

rit.

1. *a tempo*

put their trust in God a - bove. They prayed for vic - to - ry.
God kept each one safe from harm. They

rit.

a tempo

Two

2.

won the vic - to - ry.

SAMUEL THE LAMANITE

Five years before the birth of the Savior, many of the Nephites had become wicked. Even in the Church there were many wicked people. One day, a man called Samuel came to the city of Zarahemla. Samuel was a servant of the Lord, a man of great faith and righteousness, but unlike most of the other prophets of the Book of Mormon, Samuel was not a Nephite. He was a Lamanite.

He came to the people of Nephi to tell them that the Lord was not pleased with them. He preached to them and told them they had to repent. That made the people angry, and they drove Samuel out of the city. But this did not stop Samuel. He came back and climbed up on the high walls that surrounded the city. In a loud voice he cried unto the people, saying what the Lord had told him to say. He told them to repent. He also told them that in five years a sign would be given so that they would know that Jesus had been born across the sea. He said that there would be a night when the sun would go down as usual but it would not get dark. He also said that a new star would be seen in the sky.

Some of the people of Zarahemla believed Samuel and were baptized. Others tried to kill him. But the Lord protected Samuel and they could not hit him with their spears and arrows. Finally, Samuel went away and was not seen again among the Nephites. But five years later to the exact day, the sign Samuel had promised came to pass. That night, when the sun went down there was no darkness. And in the sky a bright new star shone, telling all the world that Jesus had been born. Samuel is a great example of how prophets can help us live as we should. (See Helaman 13–16, 3 Nephi 1.)

SAMUEL THE LAMANITE

MABEL JONES GABBOTT

LYNN S. LUND

Sam - uel the La - man - ite came to the Ne - phites to
Sam - uel the La - man - ite came to the Ne - phites to

born in Beth - le - hem.
from the wall and fled.
A new star will
But five years from

shine, the day will not end,
then the signs came to pass.
As signs that our Lord will
Christ came to re - deem all

come,
men,
As signs that our Lord will
Christ came to re - deem all

f

1.
come."
2.
men.

THE SAVIOR CAME TO THE NEPHITES

Thirty-four years after Christ was born in Bethlehem, the people of Nephi had become wicked once again. One day, a great storm arose in the land of America. Lightning and thunder crashed from the sky. A great earthquake shook the ground. Many cities were burned or fell to the ground or were buried. Then a great, thick darkness came upon the land. So thick was the darkness the people couldn't even light a candle or a lamp. Finally, after the three days, the darkness lifted and the people could see again.

The righteous people came to the temple in the land of Bountiful to talk about everything that had happened. Suddenly, they heard a voice from heaven. It was a still small voice. It was Heavenly Father, who said, "Behold my Beloved Son, in whom I am well pleased." As the Nephites looked up to heaven, they saw a Man coming down. At first, they thought it was an angel, but then he stretched forth his hands to them. "Behold, I am Jesus Christ," he said. It was Jesus, who had now been resurrected from the dead! Jesus let the people come to him and feel the wound in his side and also where the nails had been driven through his hands and feet. Imagine their joy to feel the body of a resurrected being.

Then Jesus began to teach them. He gave them the sacrament. He healed their sick people. He also asked for all the little children to come to him. One by one he took them in his arms and blessed them. When he was done, the heavens opened. Angels came down and circled around the little children with fire.

The Savior's visit to the Nephites is one of the most important parts of the Book of Mormon. It teaches us that Jesus Christ lives and that he cares for all of us. (See 3 Nephi 8–11, 17.)

THE SAVIOR CAME TO THE NEPHITES

GERALD N. LUND

LYNN S. LUND

THE BROTHER OF JARED

A short time after Noah and the Flood, in a country called Babel, some people decided to build a tower so they could reach heaven. This did not make God happy, so he caused all the people to talk in different languages. They couldn't understand each other anymore and they had to stop building the tower.

A man named Jared asked his brother to pray to the Lord so the language of their families and friends would not be mixed up. The brother of Jared was a righteous man and had great faith. Heavenly Father answered the prayers of the brother of Jared and did not mix up their language. He said he wanted to take the people to the promised land.

When they reached the ocean, the Lord told the brother of Jared to make eight boats so the people could sail to the promised land. The boats were small and didn't have any windows. The brother of Jared knew they had to have light, so he made sixteen small stones by melting them from the rocks. They were clear and looked like glass. He asked God to touch them so they would glow brightly and give off light inside the boats.

The brother of Jared had so much faith that when the Lord reached out to touch the stones, he saw the Lord's finger. Then he saw the Lord in all his glory. After they came to the Americas, this people, who were called the Jaredites, became a great people. But if the brother of Jared had not prayed, and then done what Heavenly Father asked him to do, the Jaredites would not have found the promised land. (See Genesis 11:1–9; Ether 1–3.)

THE BROTHER OF JARED

MABEL JONES GABBOTT

LYNN S. LUND

carry his peo - ple a - cross the sea. The bro - ther of Jar - ed said:
please give us light for our ships, we pray." The bro - ther of Jar - ed then

"We shall need light, when we're un - der the wa - ter and dark - ness is near." He
saw with his eyes the____ fin - ger of God touch each small stone with light. He

care - ful - ly gath - ered up six - teen small stones. They were melt - ed from rock, they were
trem - bled with fear and he fell to the earth, For he saw in the spir - it the

1.
white and clear.____ The

2.
Lord that night.____

WHAT DO WE KNOW ABOUT MORMON?

After Christ came to the Americas, the Nephites were righteous and lived the gospel. They had no wars and no crime. Everyone loved one another, and there were no poor people among them. For two hundred years they lived like this. But then they slowly turned bad again. By three hundred years after Jesus had come, the Nephites were very wicked. There were only a very few who still believed in Jesus and tried to keep his commandments. One of these was a ten-year-old boy named Mormon.

Because of his great faith, the Nephites made Mormon the commander of all their armies when he was sixteen, but Mormon couldn't help his people. The Nephites were so wicked now, the Lord no longer blessed them. The Lord gave Mormon a very special assignment. He told him to take all the records of the Nephites and write a shorter history of the people. He told Mormon to write about how God had worked with his people. Mormon wrote the history on gold plates, making the marks with a writing tool.

Finally, the Nephites had one last great war with the Lamanites. All the Nephites were killed, including Mormon. But by then, Mormon had finished his record and given it to his son, Moroni.

We owe a great debt to Mormon. Because of him we have the Book of Mormon and millions of people have come to know about Heavenly Father and Jesus once again. (See Mormon 1–6.)

WHAT DO WE KNOW ABOUT MORMON?

MABEL JONES GABBOTT

LYNN S. LUND

What do we know a-bout Mor - mon, Who lived in this land long a-
What do we know a-bout Mor - mon, Who lived in this land long a-

go, Where God gave his word for all peo - ple? Oh,
go, Where God gave his word for all peo - ple? Oh,

here is a man we should know. Mor - mon was brave and
here is a man we should know. Mor - mon was tall and

fear - less too. At ten he had a work to do, To care for the rec - ords
large in size. And he had faith and he was wise. He led all the ar - my

stored a - way, and write them for peo - ple in our day. What do we know a - bout
in his youth. He talked with the Lord and loved the truth. What do we know a - bout

Mor - mon? Oh, here is a man we should know.
Mor - mon? Oh, here is a man we should know.

ASK OF GOD

Before Mormon died, he gave the gold plates and all the other records to his son Moroni. Moroni was the last of the Nephite prophets. Moroni wrote a few things on the gold plates too, then buried them in the earth. There they would lie hidden for fourteen hundred years until Joseph Smith came to get them.

One of the last things Moroni wrote in the Book of Mormon was a wonderful promise. He told people how to know if the Book of Mormon is true. Moroni said that if we will pray to Heavenly Father as we read the Book of Mormon, and ask Him if it is true, we can know it is true. But we must ask with a sincere heart and real intent. That means we must really want to know if it is true. If we do that, then the Holy Ghost will tell us it is true.

Thanks to Mormon we have the Book of Mormon today. And thanks to Moroni, we also know how to find out if the Book of Mormon is the word of God. (See Moroni 10:4–5.)

ASK OF GOD

GERALD N. LUND

LYNN S. LUND

son, who was called Mo - ro - ni,_____ wrote on the gold plates too. He
prom - ise made by Mo - ro - ni was giv - en for me and you, It

told us how to find out if the Book of Mor - mon's true.
tells us how to find out if the Book of Mor - mon's true.

"And when ye shall re-ceive these things, I would ex - hort you_____ to ask of

God, In the name of Je - sus Christ, If all these things are

true. If you ask him with real in - tent, And with faith in the

Lord, God will man - i - fest the truth to you Through the

1.
pow'r of the Ho - ly Ghost." To a

2.
pow'r of the Ho - ly Ghost."

I KNOW THAT JESUS LIVES

In Moroni's promise, we are taught how to know if the Book of Mormon is true. Moroni also said that we can come to know the truth of all things in this same way. We ask God in prayer with a sincere heart. Then the Holy Ghost tells us what is true. When we know something by the power of the Holy Ghost, this is called a testimony.

One of the things the Book of Mormon teaches us is that even young children can get a testimony. They can know the gospel is true. They can know that Jesus lives and that he loves them. They can know that Joseph Smith was a prophet and that we have a living prophet on earth today.

When we have a testimony of these things from the Holy Ghost we will know how to be happy. We will live good lives and be like Jesus. And we will learn how to come back to live with our Heavenly Father and Jesus again. (See Moroni 10:5.)

I KNOW THAT JESUS LIVES

GERALD N. LUND

LYNN S. LUND

know the Book of Mor - mon is a wit - ness of Je - sus

Christ. I know the gos - pel's true.

The gos - pel is

true._____ I

true.

2.

I know that the gos - pel is

The gos - pel is

true.
true.